THE MAGNIFICENT MARIO

MIKE LEONETTI

ILLUSTRATIONS BY **GARY CHATTERTON**

SCHOLASTIC CANADA LTD.

Toronto New York London Auckland Sydney
Mexico City New Delhi Hong Kong Buenos Aires

Acknowledgements
Books written by these authors were consulted: Mike Bynum, Ron Cook, Chuck Finder, Lawrence Martin,
Dave Molinari, Paul Romanuk, Jean Somnor; Newspapers and Magazines: *The Globe and Mail*,
Pittsburgh Post-Gazette, *Sports Illustrated*, *The Hockey News*, *Toronto Star*;
Websites: hockeyreference.com, website of the QMJHL, Youtube.com, NHL.com, Hockeybuzz.com;
Videos: Minnesota North Star TV broadcasts of Game 2 and Game 6 of the 1991 Stanley Cup finals;
Record Books: *NHL Guide and Record Book*, *Total Stanley Cup*.

The hockey events depicted in this book about the career and achievements of Mario Lemieux are all true.

Scholastic Canada Ltd.
604 King Street West, Toronto, Ontario M5V 1E1, Canada

Scholastic Inc.
557 Broadway, New York, NY 10012, USA

Scholastic Australia Pty Limited
PO Box 579, Gosford, NSW 2250, Australia

Scholastic New Zealand Limited
Private Bag 94407, Botany, Manukau 2163, New Zealand

Scholastic Children's Books
Euston House, 24 Eversholt Street, London NW1 1DB, UK

Library and Archives Canada Cataloguing in Publication

Leonetti, Mike, 1958-
The magnificent Mario / Mike Leonetti ; illustrations by Gary Chatterton.

ISBN 978-1-4431-0706-8

1. Lemieux, Mario, 1965- --Juvenile fiction. I. Chatterton, Gary II. Title.

PS8573.E58734M34 2011a   jC813'.54   C2011-902073-4

6 5 4 3 2 1   Printed in Canada 114   11 12 13 14 15

This story is dedicated to Mario Lemieux —
a true hockey legend.

— M.L.

There was just a minute left in the game, but it wasn't going fast enough for me. Finally, the buzzer sounded. The Maroons celebrated their 5–1 win over our team.

I skated out to our goalie, Claude, and patted him on his helmet. He always took losing hard.

"You played a good game," I said. "Don't worry. We're just in a slump. We'll get better."

In the car, I thought about all the games we'd lost.

"Dad," I said as we pulled into the driveway. "I don't think I want to play hockey anymore." I went to my room and plopped down on my bed.

A few minutes later, my dad came in and sat next to me.

"I know you're discouraged," he said. "But Max, think about Mario Lemieux." He handed me a hockey card. Lemeiux's rookie card!

"When he joined the Pittsburgh Penguins," he said, "they were the worst team in the league. But he keeps trying to make them winners. He's taken the Penguins from being at the bottom of the league to a Stanley Cup contender. They wouldn't be there if Mario had just given up.

"Work at getting better. You might see a big change." He got up to leave. "And remember: Mario played for the Hurricanes, just like you."

He was right. I couldn't just give up.

Lemieux had lived just one street over from our house in the west end of Montreal. Dad first saw him play when Mario was only four years old. Mario took the puck down the ice, went around two defensemen and then faked the goalie out of position to score a goal. Dad couldn't believe a kid could play like that.

I started to read everything I could about Mario. He was the best player in Canada when he played junior hockey for Laval. The Penguins selected him first overall in 1984, and he recorded 100 points as a rookie. Pittsburgh didn't have a good team, but Mario still recorded 100 or more points for six straight seasons. One year he scored 86 goals!

I told the guys all about him at practice. "We can be just like Mario," I said. "He hasn't given up and neither should we. Once, the Hurricanes were down by a score of 6–1. But Mario scored 6 goals, winning the game 7–6!"

"That's a great story, but Mario's not here," Claude said.

"Yeah, but if we work hard and help each other on the ice, maybe we can start winning more games."

I was a centre like Mario, and I wanted to play just like him. He scored picture-perfect goals, and was amazing with the puck. He even challenged Wayne Gretzky as the best player in the NHL. When someone asked him about not being on a championship team, he said, "I know I'll drink from that Cup one day. I just know it."

I really wanted to believe him, but it was hard. He was injured at the start of the 1990–91 season. Most of the guys on my team thought there was no way the Pens could win without him. But Pittsburgh had built a good team. They had Jaromir Jagr, Joe Mullen, Paul Coffey, Kevin Stevens, Mark Recchi, Bryan Trottier and goalie Tom Barrasso. Late in the year Mario finally returned. It was great to see big number 66 back in action!

"Now they have a chance to win," I said to my dad as we sat in the living room watching the Pens play the Canadiens one night. And then Mario scored the first goal of the game! A couple of days later, he scored twice as the Penguins knocked the New York Rangers out of first place in their division. Mario was getting stronger at just the right time.

As for the Hurricanes, we lost a few more games, but we were also winning more often. We all felt better about the team and were working hard to get into the playoffs.

One day Coach Fichaud pulled me aside.

"Max, you're playing a good game. And I'm impressed how you've inspired your teammates."

"We've been the worst for a while," I said, "but maybe we'll get better if we believe in ourselves and the team, like Mario has for the Penguins."

In April the Pens headed to the playoffs. They beat New Jersey in the first round and then Washington in the next. It was a bit scary in the third round when they lost the first two games to Boston, but they went on to win the next four! The Penguins were headed to the Stanley Cup finals!

When the Pens lost the first game against the Minnesota North Stars, I was really disappointed. But then Dad was assigned to shoot the next game in Pittsburgh. "Hey, Max, why don't you come with me? I know someone who can get us a ticket."

A chance to see Mario play in the Stanley Cup finals!

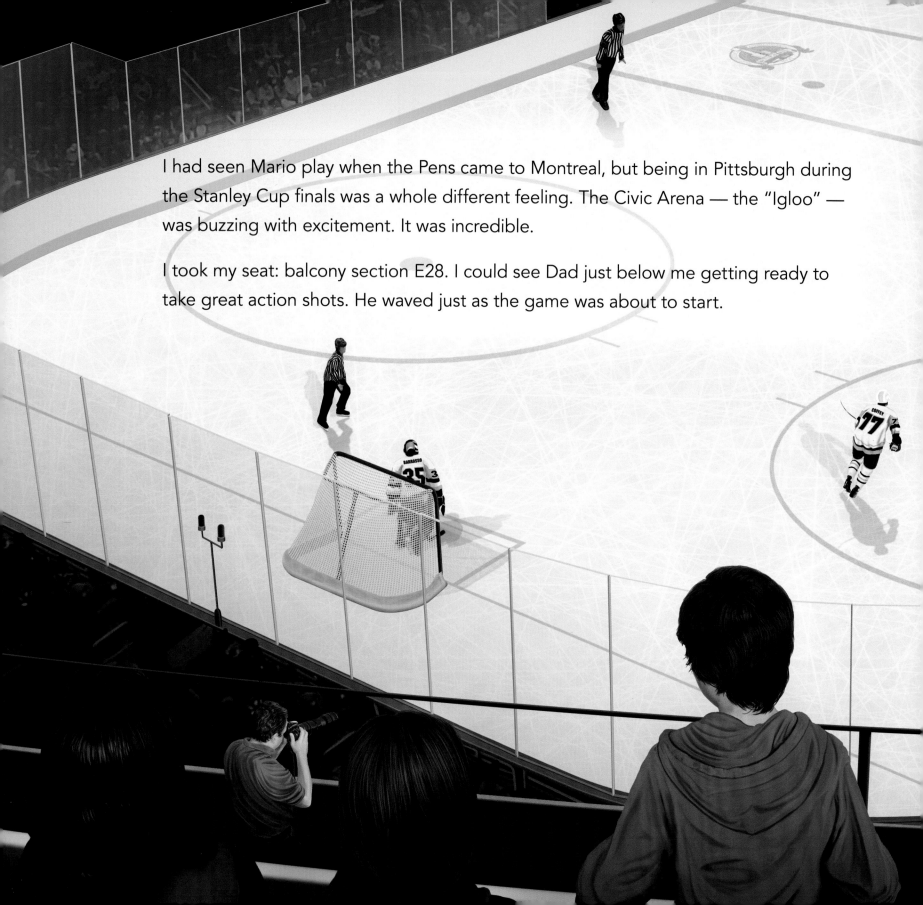

I had seen Mario play when the Pens came to Montreal, but being in Pittsburgh during the Stanley Cup finals was a whole different feeling. The Civic Arena — the "Igloo" — was buzzing with excitement. It was incredible.

I took my seat: balcony section E28. I could see Dad just below me getting ready to take great action shots. He waved just as the game was about to start.

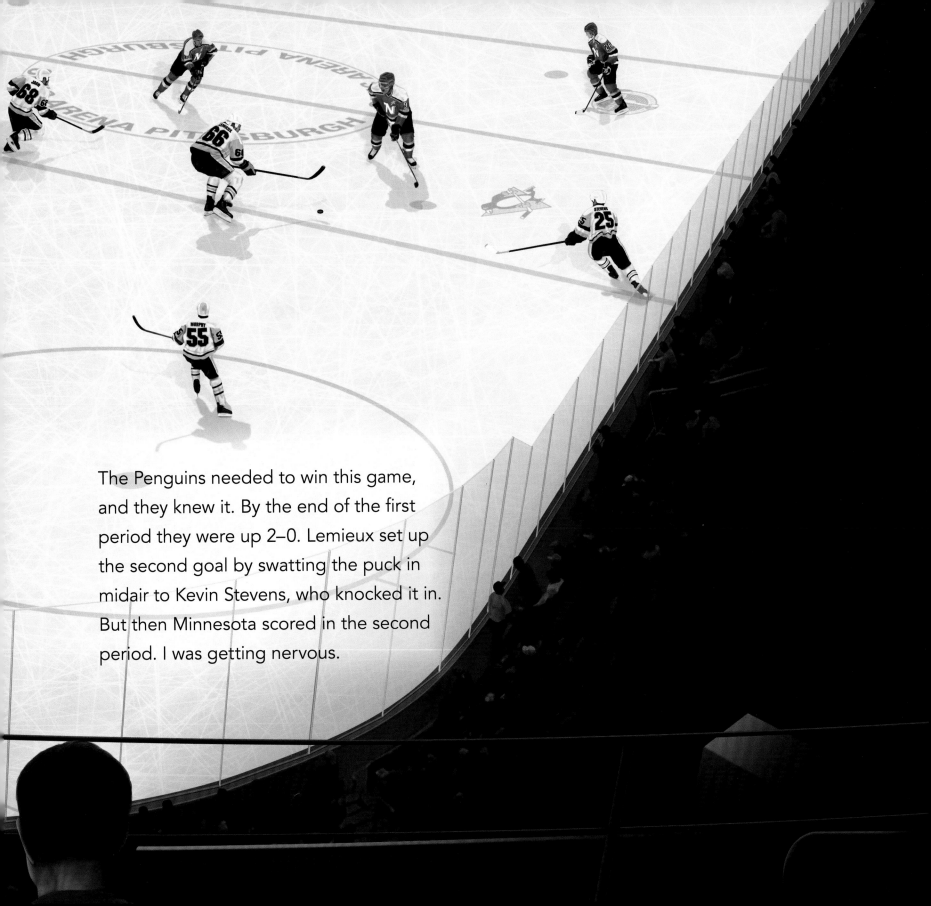

The Penguins needed to win this game, and they knew it. By the end of the first period they were up 2–0. Lemieux set up the second goal by swatting the puck in midair to Kevin Stevens, who knocked it in. But then Minnesota scored in the second period. I was getting nervous.

In the second period, Mario took the puck from his own end and sped straight up the ice. There were two North Star defensemen waiting for him at the Minnesota blueline, but one of them backed away a little as he charged toward the net. Mario got the puck past the other defender by putting it through the defender's legs, then went in all alone on the goalie and waited for him to make his move. Mario used his long reach to keep the puck away — and then backhanded a shot into the net!

Mario went down on the ice. But he was up in a flash, pumping his arm in the air. What a goal! We all jumped to our feet, too. Only the great Mario could score like that!

Minnesota never challenged Mario's magnificent goal, and the Penguins tied the series with a 4–1 victory.

21

On the plane ride home, all Dad and I talked about was Mario.

"I remember New Year's Eve, 1988," he said. "That night Mario scored five goals in five different ways: at even strength, short-handed, on a power play, on a penalty shot and then into an empty net. Nobody has ever done that. Pittsburgh won the game 8–6, and Mario was in on every goal," Dad said.

"I've seen some great players," he continued. "But I think Mario may be the best."

"I just hope he wins the Stanley Cup," I said. "Until then, he won't be thought of as a truly great player."

Back home, my skating, passing and shooting skills improved. My teammates seemed to get better, too. In practice, we stressed team play. The Hurricanes kept playing hard no matter what the score was, and we won more games. We even got the last playoff spot! In our game against the Maroons, we were down 4–2 heading into the third period, but we kept coming at them. We scored two goals, and I scored in the last minute to win 5–4 and knock them out of the playoffs. We celebrated like we'd won a championship!

In the second round, we were eliminated. It was disappointing, but after such a bad start to the season, we knew we'd gotten a lot better.

Mario missed his next game with an injury, and the Penguins lost. After he came back, Pittsburgh took a 3–2 lead in the series. The sixth game was in Minnesota, and again Dad was assigned to shoot the game. This time I stayed home and watched it on TV.

The Penguins opened the scoring just two minutes in when Joe Mullen scored. Then Mario took a long pass and galloped past the North Star defense to score another one of his amazing goals to make it 2–0. Mario set up three more goals with great passes. The Penguins won 8–0! Mario had finally won the Cup — just like he said he would!

Mario also won the Conn Smythe Trophy as the best player in the playoffs, but it was the Stanley Cup he really wanted. He towered over it as it was set on a table at centre ice. Finally he raised the Cup over his head and was mobbed by his teammates.

When Dad came home, he gave me a photograph he had taken of Mario. When Mario brought the Cup to the neighbourhood for a day, he signed my picture.

I put the photo on my dresser. Seeing it every day reminded me that winning is possible if you stick to it. I imagined holding a championship trophy of my own. We had almost done it this season. Maybe next season we could raise our own trophy just like Mario and the Penguins.

About Mario Lemieux

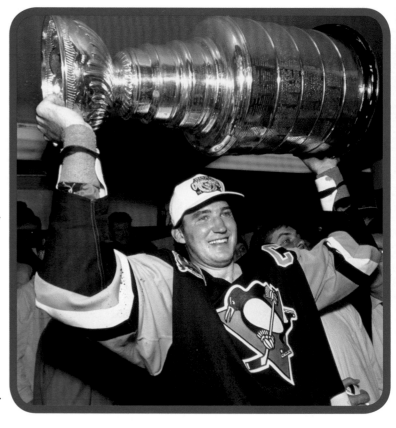

Mario Lemieux was born in Montreal on October 5, 1965, and played minor hockey in Ville Emard, where he grew up. He played junior hockey for the Laval Voisins of the Quebec Major Junior Hockey League, recording 282 points (133 goals, 149 assists) in 70 games during the 1983–84 season. He was selected first overall by the Pittsburgh Penguins in the 1984 NHL Entry Draft, and the 6'4", 230-pound Lemieux had the hopes of a troubled franchise placed on his broad shoulders. Although he was shy and spoke little English at the time, he let his talent do all the talking on the ice. He scored a goal on his first shift in his first NHL game on October 11, 1984, against the Boston Bruins. He finished his first year with 100 points and won the Calder Trophy as the best rookie in the league. The Penguins made the playoffs only once in his first six years, but then won the Stanley Cup in 1991 and 1992, with Mario taking the Conn Smythe Trophy both times. During the 1992–93 season, Mario was diagnosed with Hodgkin's lymphoma, a form of cancer. After receiving radiation treatments, Lemieux returned to play and finished the year as the NHL's leading scorer with 160 points in just 60 games played. He would lead the league in points six times and be named the most valuable player on three occasions. The nine time all-star (six times on the first team) was also a part of Team Canada when they won the Canada Cup (1987), the gold medal at the Olympics (2002) and the World Cup (2004). He initially announced his retirement from the NHL after the 1996–97 season and was elected to the Hall of Fame in 1997. He decided to come back in the 2000–01 season and retired for good after the 2005–06 campaign. Lemieux finished with 690 goals and 1,033 assists for a total of 1,723 points in 915 games played. He scored 50 or more goals on six occasions and recorded 100 or more points ten times during his illustrious career. After his retirement Lemieux became a part owner of the Pittsburgh club and in 2009, the Penguins won the Stanley Cup for the third time in their history.